FOLENS GEOGRAPHY HIGHLIGHTS

Geography for Juniors 2

John Corn

Contents

Folens Publishers

United Kingdom: Folens Publishers, Apex Business Centre, Boscombe Road, Dunstable, LU5 4RL.
Email: folens@folens.com

Ireland: Folens Publishers, Greenhills Road, Tallaght, Dublin 24.
Email: info@folens.ie

Poland: JUKA, ul. Renesansowa 38, Warsaw 01-905.

Editor: Katharine Jacobson
Layout artists: Suzanne Ward and Patricia Hollingsworth
Cover design: Martin Cross
Cover picture: Simon Fraser/Science Photo Library
Illustrations: Gary Clifford

First published 2002 by Folens Limited.

British Library Cataloguing in Publication Data. A catalogue record for this publication is available from the British Library.

ISBN 1 84303 155 8

Introduction

Geography Highlights presents units from the QCA scheme of work and Curriculum 2000 in activities that are accessible to children in the Infant and Junior phases. Through the units selected, **Geography Highlights** focuses on the concepts, skills and knowledge in Geography that enable children to build up referencing and organisational skills relating to any region or topic in Geography as a whole.

Geography for Juniors 2 is aimed at children aged 9–11 (Y4/6, P6/7). It highlights units 11–25 of the QCA scheme of work (see below).

Each unit comprises:

Ideas page
This teacher-reference page sets out the essential background to the unit with learning objectives and lesson notes for each activity sheet. There is a section on introducing and using the activity sheet and suggestions for follow-up and extension work. The symbol **F** is used to denote activities involving fieldwork, though it is recognised that in some cases the first-hand experience of a field trip may need to be replaced by or supplemented with information from reference books or on-line sources. It is also recognised that some of this research may be undertaken by children working independently either in class or at home. A useful reference tool for children's research on the Internet and on-line sources is *Online Geography* by John Lancaster (Belair BA0309).

Activity sheets
The three activity sheets for each of the units aim to provide information, processes and model-layout tools for researching, organising and presenting information in Geography. Folens Atlases UK, (F841X) and World, (F3302) would provide valuable support in completing these.

Units from the QCA Geography scheme of work covered in *Geography for Juniors 2*

11 Water	**12** Should the high street be closed to traffic?	**13** A contrasting UK locality	**14** Investigating rivers	**15** The mountain environment
16 What's in the news?	**17** Global eye	**18** Connecting ourselves to the world	**19** How and where do we spend our time?	**20** Local traffic – an environmental issue
21 How can we improve the environment we can see from our window?	**22** A contrasting locality overseas	**23** Investigating coasts	**24** Passport to the world	**25** Geography and numbers

Background

The activity sheets are based on a map of the locality (similar to a 1:50 000 scale map), a plan of the school and a water-usage survey. Local examples of these could be used to promote work close to home.

The children are encouraged to recognise the importance of water in our daily lives, including where it can be found in the locality and how we rely on it being readily available to us both in school and at home.

Learning Objectives

- To identify water features on a local map.
- To use plans and maps of different scales.
- To use secondary sources.
- To collect and record data.

Water, Water Everywhere

Introducing and using the sheet
- Talk about the forms that water takes in the environment, such as rivers, ponds and marshes. Ask the children to come up with local examples.
- Look together at a local 1:50 000 (or 1:25 000) scale map. Locate the school and other places known to the children.
- Ask the children to find places close to the school where they would find water. (To focus on one part of the map, use a 'frame' or 'window' cut out from a piece of plain or cm² graph paper.)

Follow-up/extension ideas
- List the features found on the local map. Ask the children to identify each feature and give it a six-figure grid reference.
- Ask the children to make a local water-features map. They should trace the features that they can locate inside the frame and label each one.
- F Visit some of the water features that are close to the school. Take photographs, annotate them, and attach them to the local map.

Waterwell Primary School

Introducing and using the sheet
- Discuss with the children how water is used in school, for example when and where most is used, how water comes into the school and how it leaves. Find out where the meters and stop valves are and ask the caretaker to show the children.
- Hand around some water bills received by the school. See how much water the school uses and how much it costs.
- Talk about the water features on the activity sheet. Describe what each looks like and why it is needed.

Follow-up/extension ideas
- Conduct a water-usage survey in your school. The children should make a plan similar to that in the activity sheet and then colour code the different usages.
- Ask groups of children to consider how the school could reduce the amount of water used. Groups should present their ideas to the class.

Water Explorer

Introducing and using the sheet
- In pairs, the children should make a list of how water is used at home and in the garden.
- Show the children a litre of water, so that they have an idea of its volume, and ask them to estimate how much water is involved in the uses they have listed.
- Ask the children to look at the activity sheet to see how much water is used to do some basic household jobs and then to calculate how accurate their estimates were.
- The children should complete the **Water Explorer** survey over one week.

Follow-up/extension ideas
- Ask the children to make posters showing how water could be saved at home.
- As a class, measure how much water a dripping tap wastes. Collect water for 5 minutes in a measuring jug and then use this to calculate how much is wasted in an hour, a day, a week, and so on. Ask the children to consider how many baths, showers, or toilet flushes this equates to. The results could be recorded in spreadsheet graphs.

Water, Water Everywhere

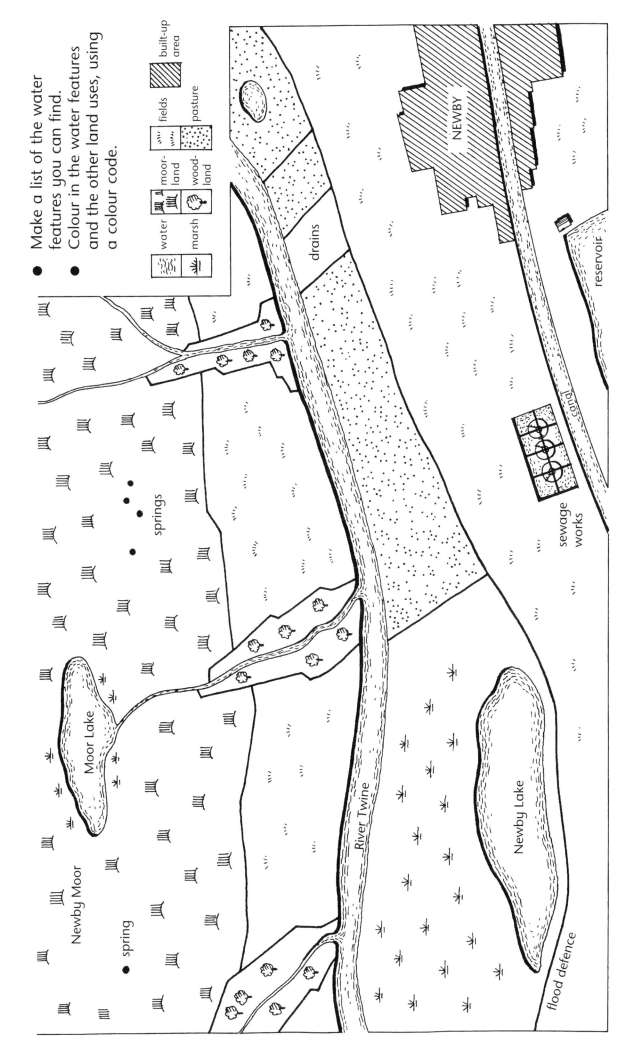

- Make a list of the water features you can find.
- Colour in the water features and the other land uses, using a colour code.

fields

built-up area

moor-land

woodland

water

marsh

pasture

NEWBY

drains

reservoir

canal

sewage works

springs

Moor Lake

River Twine

Newby Lake

Newby Moor

spring

flood defence

Waterwell Primary School

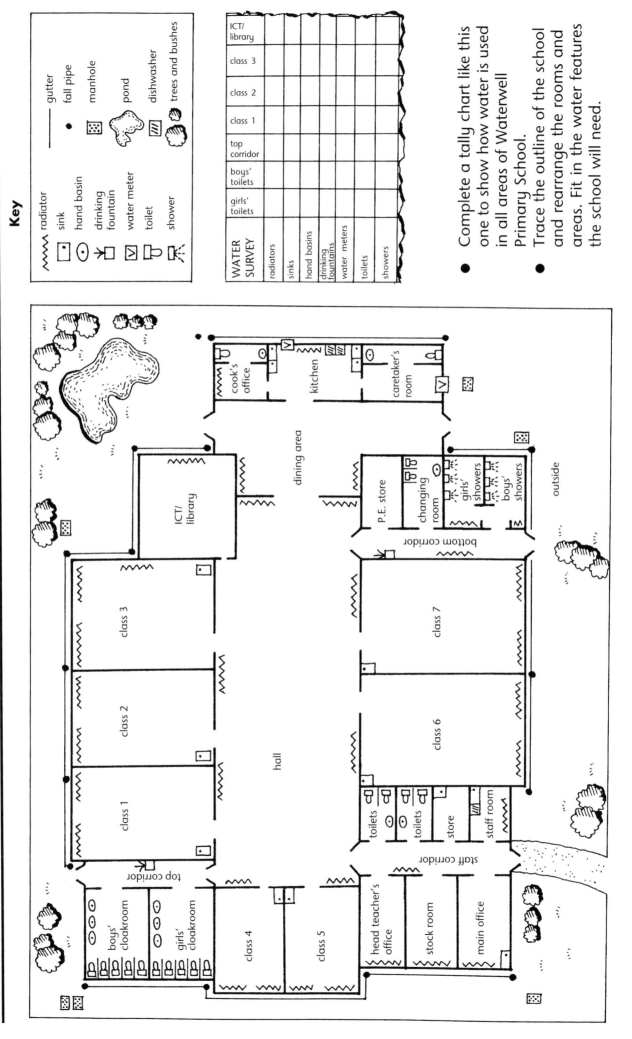

Key

- radiator
- sink
- hand basin
- drinking fountain
- water meter
- toilet
- shower
- gutter
- fall pipe
- manhole
- pond
- dishwasher
- trees and bushes

WATER SURVEY	girls' toilets	boys' toilets	top corridor	class 1	class 2	class 3	ICT/ library
radiators							
sinks							
hand basins							
drinking fountains							
water meters							
toilets							
showers							

- Complete a tally chart like this one to show how water is used in all areas of Waterwell Primary School.
- Trace the outline of the school and rearrange the rooms and areas. Fit in the water features the school will need.

Geography Highlights for Juniors 2
© Folens (copiable page)

Water Explorer

TALLY CHART	washing machine 80 litres	dish washer 35 litres	toilet flush 9 litres	bath 120 litres	car wash (by hand) 30 litres	washing up 10 litres	shower 20 litres	cleaning teeth 5 litres	cooking and drinking
SUNDAY									10 litres
MONDAY									10 litres
TUESDAY									10 litres
WEDNESDAY									10 litres
THURSDAY									10 litres
FRIDAY									10 litres
SATURDAY									10 litres
TOTAL									

GRAND WEEKLY TOTAL =

Background

The activity sheets **Clean-up Time** and **Clean Enough to Drink** explore the themes of maintaining a clean water supply, and its treatment and distribution, in economically developed countries. **Not Enough to Drink** shows how irrigation is used to bring water to drier areas and considers the advantages and disadvantages of watering crops in different ways. Some basic science research equipment will be needed to complete **Clean-up Time**, while **Clean Enough to Drink** will be enhanced by a visit to a water-treatment works.

Learning Objectives

- To collect and clean samples of water.
- To record data from investigations.
- To understand the process of cleaning and distributing water.
- To use secondary sources.
- To review how efficient and effective different forms of irrigation are.

Clean-up Time

Introducing and using the sheet

⚠ *The children should not taste dirty water.*

- Discuss with the children what makes water dirty and where they would find dirty water.
- Show the children a sample of dirty water and ask them to think about how they would attempt to clean it. Discuss their ideas.
- Ask the children to think about what may be in the water that cannot be seen, for example bacteria.

Follow-up/extension ideas

- Ask the children to write up the experiment from the activity sheet.
- With the children watching, collect samples of dirty water from around the school. Ask the children to assess how dirty the samples are, using a scale from 1 for quite clean to 5 for very dirty, and why this might be. They should note how each sample smells.
- Conduct some research into the health effects of drinking dirty water. The children can use the library or ICT to find out about times when people did not have clean water, how it affected their lives and what changes helped ensure a cleaner water supply. They could also find out about places affected by dirty water today.

Clean Enough to Drink

Introducing and using the sheet

- Talk about what happens when we pull out the plug in a bath or a sink or flush the toilet.
- Help the children to find a sewage or water-treatment works on a local map and estimate the distance to it from school. Explain the water-cleaning process employed by the works.
- Ask the caretaker to raise manhole covers around the school and show small groups of children the network of drains. Safety is paramount.

Follow-up/extension ideas

- **F** Arrange a visit to a local water-treatment works. The children should record the treatment process and label a base plan of the site.
- Ask the children to construct a flow chart showing the process of changing dirty into clean water.
- Show the children a local map, 1:50 000 or 1:25 000 scale, and ask them to locate all the services concerned with the storage, treatment and distribution of clean water to houses in your town.

Not Enough to Drink

Introducing and using the sheet

- Ask the children to find out where the hot, dry countries are, using an atlas, CD-ROMs or the Internet.
- Talk about the difficulties of growing crops in these parts of the world with their poor soils, little water and high rates of evaporation caused by high daytime temperatures.
- Instigate a class discussion about how crops could be watered under these conditions. The activity sheet can then be completed in pairs. [1 – wasteful; 2 – expensive but easily controlled; 3 – wasteful, labour-intensive but cheap; 4 – inefficient but cheap.]

Follow-up/extension ideas

- Encourage discussion about other economical ways to water crops in dry areas (such as dripping pipes laid alongside plants, or screens to reduce evaporation).
- Conduct experiments to discover how little water a plant needs to grow. The children should think about ways of reducing evaporation and watering at different times of the day.

Clean-up Time

Conduct an investigation into cleaning dirty water:
- Colour in the sample square the colour of the dirty water before it is filtered.
- Pour 100ml of dirty water through each of the four funnels containing:
    1. filter paper
    2. cotton wool
    3. sand
    4. gravel.
- Colour in the filtered water in each of the beakers shown.
- Which substance best cleans dirty water?

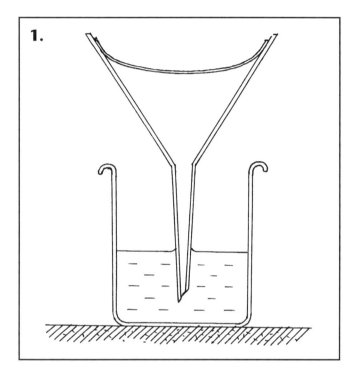

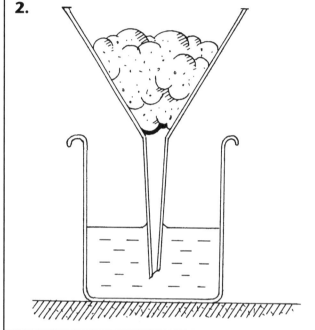

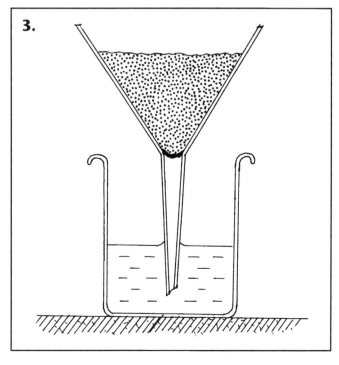

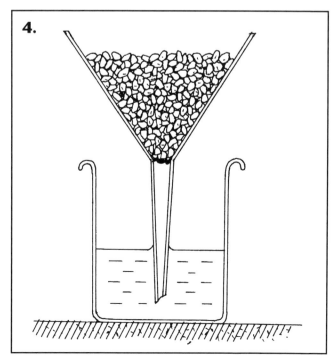

Clean Enough to Drink

Water from reservoirs and rivers has to be cleaned before it can be used. This is done at a water-treatment works.

● Fill in the speech balloons to show what the guide might be saying at each of the stopping points. You may need another piece of paper for this.

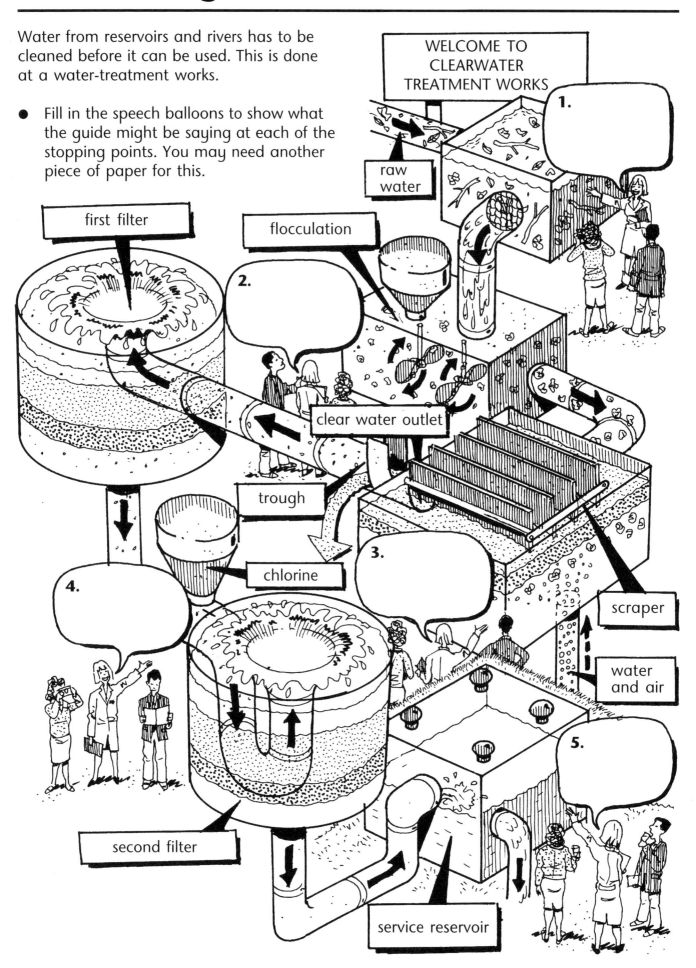

Geography Highlights for Juniors 2 © Folens (copiable page)

Not Enough to Drink

In hot, dry countries different ways of watering, or 'irrigating', crops are used to make them grow.

- Look at each of these ways of watering crops.
- Describe each method and say what its advantages and disadvantages are.
- Which method do you think is the best?

Traffic in a Busy Street

This is a small-scale investigation that involves the children using fieldwork skills to assess the impact of traffic in a busy street. They are encouraged to consider the views of people affected by it and to devise alternative routes for traffic around the High Street. Similar investigations can be undertaken near school.

Learning Objectives

- To investigate a place.
- To undertake fieldwork.
- To make decisions and explain them.
- To consider the views of people centrally involved.

High Street Blues

Introducing and using the sheet

- Talk about the charts and statistics on the sheet. What does each say about traffic conditions on the High Street? What do the children think of the suggestions on the police report?
- Talk about the traffic around your local shopping centre. Consider how much there is, where it is coming from and going to, why it passes through, who benefits from it and who loses.

Follow-up/extension ideas

- F Conduct a local traffic survey. Ask the children to look at the volume of traffic, parking problems and problems caused by noise and pollution. Collect the views of local shoppers and shopkeepers.
- The children should present the data in a display.

Bumper to Bumper

Introducing and using the sheet

- Encourage pairs of children to construct profiles of the types of people affected by traffic in the High Street – for example, shopkeepers, parents with young children, delivery people, taxi drivers and traffic wardens. What does each group need from the High Street to make life easier or more profitable? For example, a shopkeeper may need lots of customers, plenty of parking, nearby banks and access for delivery vans. The children should complete the activity sheet in their pairs.
- Talk about the environmental effects of traffic in the High Street. You could organise a class debate or invite members of the public to come in and speak for and against the traffic.

Follow-up/extension ideas

- Make a display showing the different comments about traffic in the High Street made by class members during the discussions. Decorate it with pictures of different forms of traffic.
- F In your local High Street, ask the children to take photographs and collect comments from people who are affected by traffic. Back in class, make a display.

Diversion

Introducing and using the sheet

- This is an extension to **Bumper to Bumper**. It looks at the implications of diverting traffic should the High Street become pedestrianised.
- Ask the children to suggest ways of keeping traffic away from their local shopping centre.
- Discuss current local initiatives aimed at reducing or eliminating traffic, such as park-and-ride schemes, bus lanes and expensive car parks.
- Look together at the activity sheet. Focus in particular on the section of the High Street between the two black lines, which is the proposed traffic-free area. Ask pairs of children to consider alternative routes around this section of the High Street and to mark their preferred route in colour.

Follow-up/extension ideas

- Ask some pairs of children to describe their diversion and explain the decisions they had to make when constructing the route. They could then use a DTP package to make a newspaper feature about it.
- The children should measure their proposed diversion and work out how much further the traffic would have to go.

High Street Blues

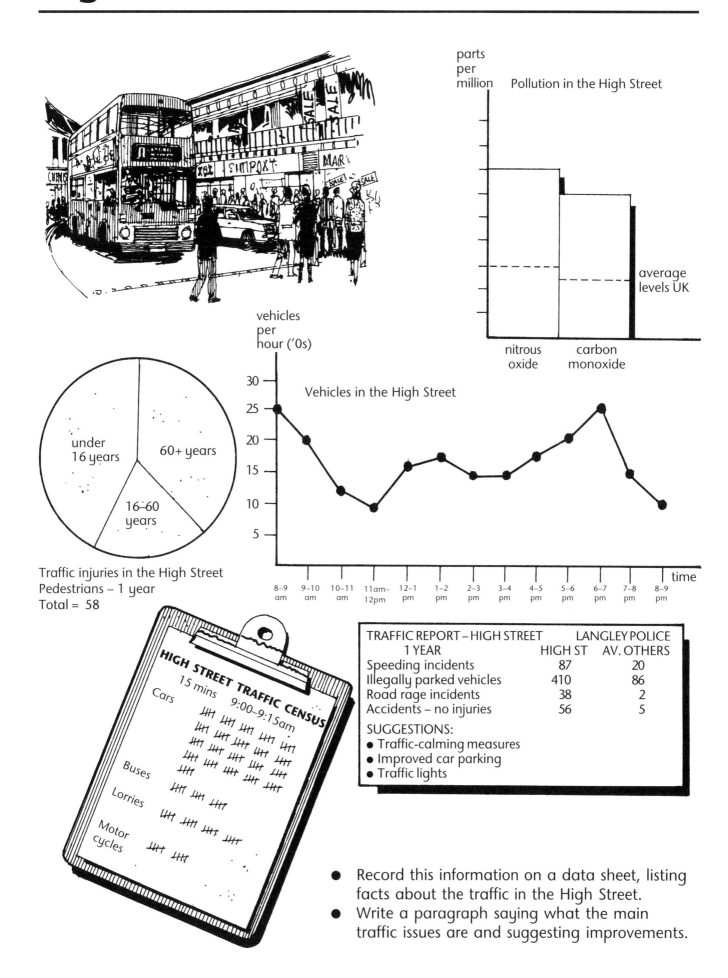

parts per million

Pollution in the High Street

average levels UK

nitrous oxide   carbon monoxide

vehicles per hour ('0s)

Vehicles in the High Street

30
25
20
15
10
5

time

8–9 am | 9–10 am | 10–11 am | 11am–12pm | 12–1 pm | 1–2 pm | 2–3 pm | 3–4 pm | 4–5 pm | 5–6 pm | 6–7 pm | 7–8 pm | 8–9 pm

under 16 years

60+ years

16–60 years

Traffic injuries in the High Street
Pedestrians – 1 year
Total = 58

HIGH STREET TRAFFIC CENSUS
15 mins   9:00–9:15am

Cars
卌 卌 卌 卌
卌 卌 卌 卌 卌
卌 卌 卌 卌 卌
卌 卌 卌 卌 卌
Buses   卌 卌 卌 卌 卌
Lorries   卌 卌 卌
卌 卌 卌 卌 卌
Motor cycles   卌 卌

TRAFFIC REPORT – HIGH STREET	LANGLEY POLICE	
1 YEAR	HIGH ST	AV. OTHERS
Speeding incidents	87	20
Illegally parked vehicles	410	86
Road rage incidents	38	2
Accidents – no injuries	56	5

SUGGESTIONS:
- Traffic-calming measures
- Improved car parking
- Traffic lights

- Record this information on a data sheet, listing facts about the traffic in the High Street.
- Write a paragraph saying what the main traffic issues are and suggesting improvements.

Bumper to Bumper

- In each speech balloon write what the person might say about traffic in the High Street.
- Think who else may be affected by traffic in the High Street. Draw a large speech balloon for each and write in it what the person thinks about the traffic.

Diversion

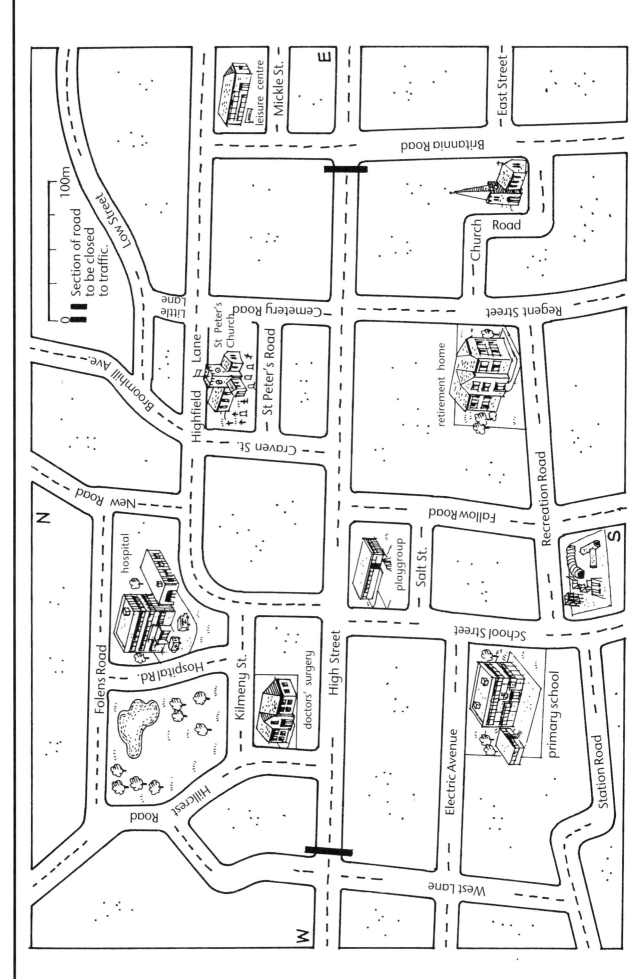

A Contrasting UK Locality 1

Background

These three activity sheets, and those in the following unit, look at the nature of a particular place and encourage the children to compare and contrast it with their own locality. Both sets of sheets explore Bingley, a small West Yorkshire town that maintains its character despite the proximity of larger towns and cities. In this unit the sheets focus on routes to Bingley, its general characteristics and its land uses.

Learning Objectives

- To investigate the characteristics of different places.
- To identify physical and human features.
- To use and interpret maps.
- To generalise about land use.
- To construct a generalised land-use field sketch.

Routemaster

Introducing and using the sheet
- A collection of road atlases will be needed. Children can work in pairs.
- Talk about journeys by car, using a road atlas, and the importance of clear road signs. On a local map look at the road network around your town and ask the children to estimate distances between places.
- Now get the children to measure the distances they have estimated using string or a strip of paper. They should then use the scale to calculate other distances. Talk about the likely road conditions and ask the children to estimate journey times. Look at the activity sheet and try an example together.

Follow-up/extension ideas
- Try the exercise in reverse. Supply 'Routemaster' information from Bingley to a mystery destination and ask the children to locate it using their road atlases.
- Look at Bingley in the road atlas and ask the children how busy with traffic they think it will be. A dual carriageway is planned. Ask the children to plot its likely route through Bingley using a street map.

Time Out

Introducing and using the sheet
- Look together at the activity sheet and discuss what attractions there are around Bingley.
- Ask the children, in pairs, to brainstorm their expectations of Bingley based on their road atlas, the map and the advertisements around it.

Follow-up/extension ideas
- Ask the children to describe Bingley and the surrounding area in terms of landscape, settlements and communications.
- Hand out local large-scale (1:1 250 or 1:2 500) Ordnance Survey maps and leaflets from the tourist information office for the children to use to produce their own 'Time Out' posters of your town.
- Ask the children how your town compares with Bingley. Make a display advertising your town as a tourist attraction. The children could produce leaflets using a DTP package and scanning images.

Looking Around

Introducing and using the sheet
- Ask the children what land uses they can see on the field sketch. Together, work out some categories of land use in and around Bingley [industry, woodland, fields, quarries, residential, allotments, shops, school and playing fields, open space and transport]. The children should draw a colour-coded land-use map of Bingley.

Follow-up/extension ideas
- Ask the children to rank the land uses found in Bingley according to how much land they take up (start with the one that takes most).
- Look together at a local map of 1:50 000 or 1:25 000 scale. Put a 'frame' around your town and immediate surroundings and ask the children to make a local land-use map.
- The children should then rank the land uses found and compare them to those found in the field sketch and land-use map of Bingley.

Routemaster

- Use a road atlas to work out the shortest journey from each of these places to Bingley. Fill in each road to be taken and where to change to the next road until the final destination is reached.

<<ROUTEMASTER>>
HARROGATE TO BINGLEY

Road   to   Place

Distance km ☐ Estimated journey time ☐

<<ROUTEMASTER>>
NEWCASTLE TO BINGLEY

Road   to   Place

Distance km ☐ Estimated journey time ☐

<<ROUTEMASTER>>
GLASGOW TO BINGLEY

Road   to   Place

Distance km ☐ Estimated journey time ☐

<<ROUTEMASTER>>
CARDIFF TO BINGLEY

Road   to   Place

Distance km ☐ Estimated journey time ☐

NEW ROAD ATLAS
ROUTEMASTER

Time Out

- Try to locate the tourist attractions on the map and give a six-figure grid reference for each.
- Give references for other places you can find near Bingley.

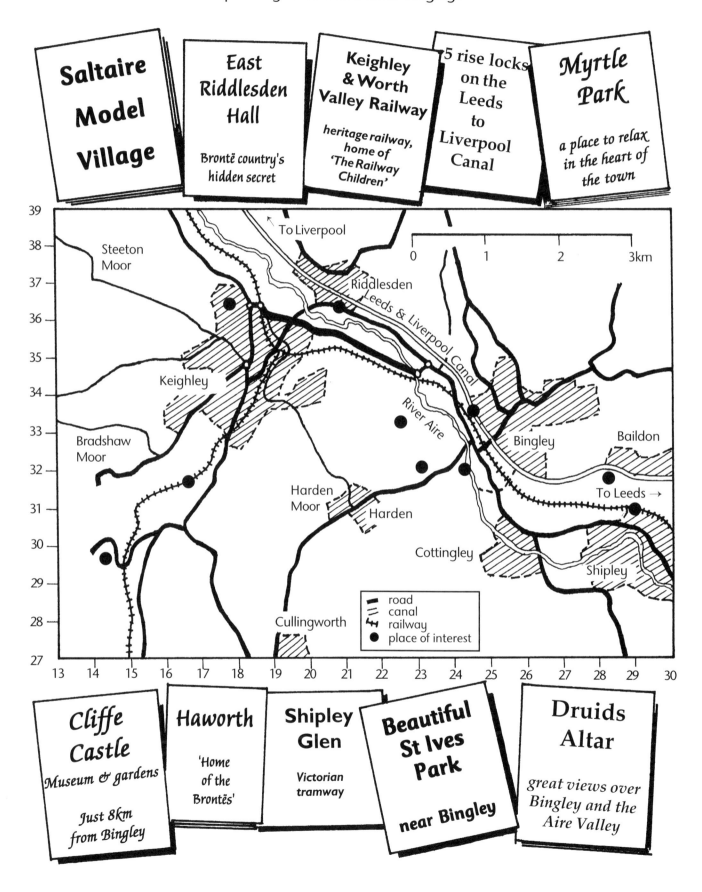

Saltaire Model Village

East Riddlesden Hall

Brontë country's hidden secret

Keighley & Worth Valley Railway

heritage railway, home of 'The Railway Children'

5 rise locks on the Leeds to Liverpool Canal

Myrtle Park

a place to relax in the heart of the town

Cliffe Castle

Museum & gardens

Just 8km from Bingley

Haworth

'Home of the Brontës'

Shipley Glen

Victorian tramway

Beautiful St Ives Park

near Bingley

Druids Altar

great views over Bingley and the Aire Valley

Looking Around

● Look carefully at the field sketch of Bingley. Make a general land-use map of the town and add a colour code.

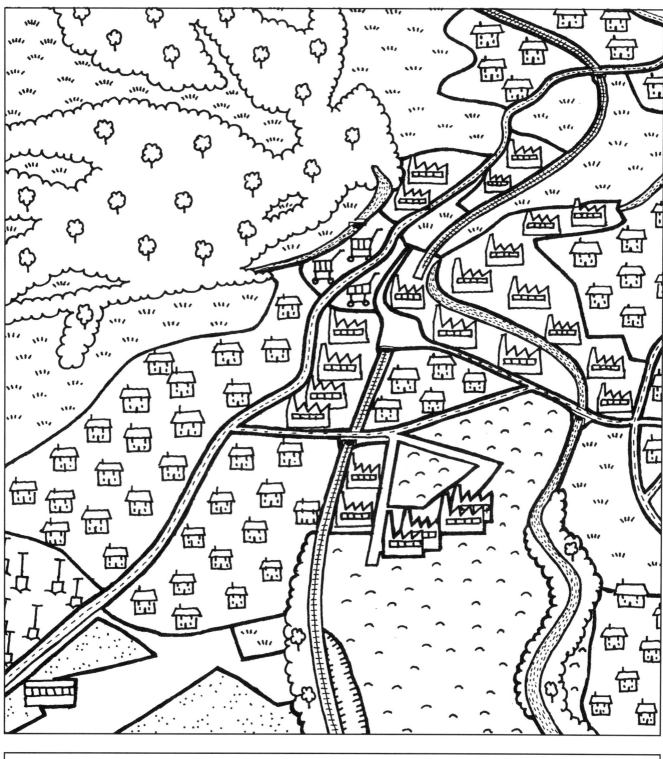

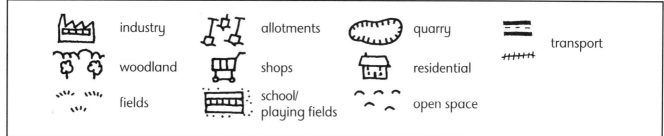

industry

woodland

fields

allotments

shops

school/
playing fields

quarry

residential

open space

transport

A Contrasting UK Locality 2

Background

Following on from the previous unit, these three activity sheets further explore the theme of urban land use. Now the children are encouraged to compare how the land uses in Bingley compare with those in rural areas (and, again, to compare Bingley with their own town).

Learning Objectives

- To identify, record and compare land uses.
- To make thematic maps using colour coding and explain the patterns that emerge.
- To appreciate the nature of a settlement that is different to their own.
- To make comparisons between environments.

Land Use

Introducing and using the sheet
- Discuss the land uses in your school and its locality. Ask the children which they think are the most important. Conduct a land-use survey in the school using an outline plan and a colour code. Take photographs of different land uses and attach them to the plan.
- Look together at the activity sheet and talk about the important land uses in and around the town centre of Bingley. Look for patterns of land use in the town.

Follow-up/extension ideas
- [F] Conduct a local land-use survey using a large-scale 1:1250 map of your area. Ask the children to record land use on a base map and take photographs to show different local land uses. Make a display of the findings.
- Encourage the children to think about how their local land-use map and that of Bingley might compare with one of a village or city.

Retail Therapy

Introducing and using the sheet
- Ask the children to think about the shops in their local area and put them into general categories. Remind the children that some shops sell a variety of goods and so should be categorised according to what they use most floor space for.
- Now the children should look at the shops on the activity sheet and put them into categories using a colour code [food retail, food services, finance, electrical, furniture, clothes, medical, other specialists, empty].

Follow-up/extension ideas
- [F] Conduct a similar survey at a nearby shopping centre (an area with at least 20 shops). Use a simplified base plan taken from a 1:1250 scale map. The children should use the same colour code as on the activity sheet. Back in class, compare the results.
- [F] In the shopping centre, ask the children to take photographs of the shops and collect advertisements from them to make a frieze. Ask them also to interview shoppers about where they live, what they are buying and how often they shop there.
  The results should be recorded in maps and graphs on return to school.

Bingley Trail

Introducing and using the sheet
- Ask the children to cut out the sketches, captions and map from the activity sheet and match up the sketches and captions [1–E, 2–I, 3–A, 4–J, 5–G, 6–H, 7–C, 8–F, 9–B, 10–D].
- Enlarge the map and ask the children to make (using the sketches and captions) a poster or leaflet entitled 'A Tourist Guide to Bingley'. It should describe a walk around the town, with stopping points marked in.

Follow-up/extension ideas
- Ask the children which places they would put in a local tourist leaflet and why. They should ask local people for their views and make a spreadsheet chart of the most popular and interesting places.
- The children could make a poster or leaflet similar to the one they made of Bingley but for the area close to school.
- Ask groups to look at the similarities and differences between Bingley and your local town, concentrating on land use, economic activity, buildings and communication.

Land Use

- Look carefully at the land-use map of Bingley. Colour the boxes in the key and then colour the map accordingly.
- Describe each of the land-use sketches, using the key. Locate where each one might be on the map and join them with a straight line.

BINGLEY

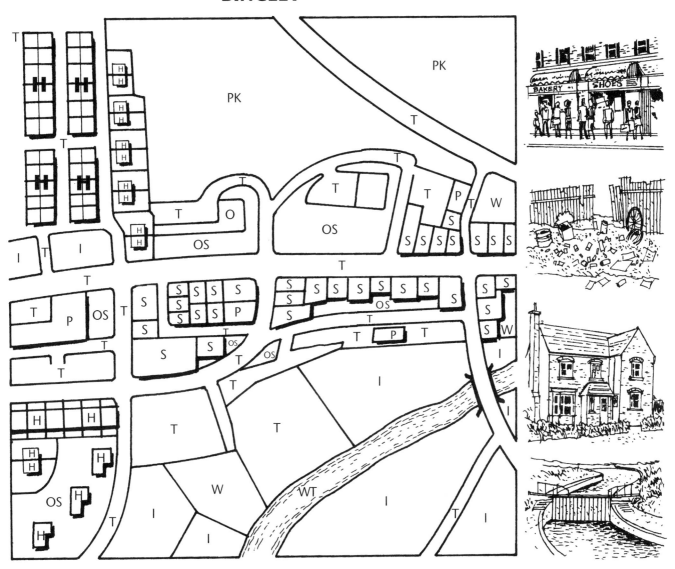

Land-use key

H	Housing	OS	Open space	S	Shop	I	Industrial land	
T	Transport	PK	Park	W	Waste land			
O	Office	P	Public building	WT	Water			

Retail Therapy

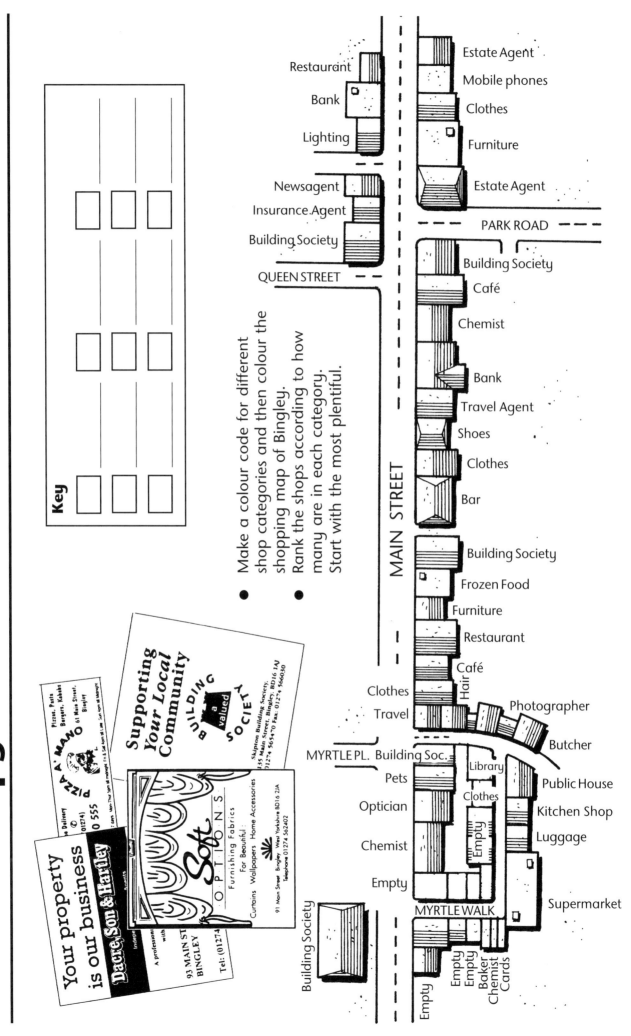

* Make a colour code for different shop categories and then colour the shopping map of Bingley.
* Rank the shops according to how many are in each category. Start with the most plentiful.

Key

QUEEN STREET

Restaurant
Bank
Lighting

Newsagent
Insurance Agent
Building Society

Estate Agent
Mobile phones
Clothes
Furniture
Estate Agent

PARK ROAD

Building Society
Café
Chemist
Bank
Travel Agent
Shoes
Clothes
Bar

MAIN STREET

Building Society
Frozen Food
Furniture
Restaurant
Café
Hair
Photographer
Butcher

Clothes
Travel

MYRTLE PL. Building Soc.
Pets
Optician
Chemist
Empty

Library
Clothes
Empty

Public House
Kitchen Shop
Luggage
Supermarket

MYRTLE WALK

Building Society

Empty
Empty Empty
Baker Chemist Cards

Your property is our business

Dacre, Son & Hartley

Indep... Agents

A professional ...
with

93 MAIN ST
BINGLEY

Tel: (0127...

PIZZA A' MANO
Pizza, Pasta
Burgers, Kebabs
61 Main Street,
Bingley

... Delivery
(0) 555
(01274)
... 9am – Mon–Thur 5pm til midnight Fri & Sat 4pm till 1 am Sun 4pm til Midnight

Supporting Your Local Community

BUILDING SOCIETY
a valued

Skipton Building Society,
135 Main Street, Bingley. BD16 1AV
01274 565470 Fax: 01274 566030

Soft OPTIONS
Furnishing Fabrics
For Beautiful:
Curtains Wallpapers Home Accessories

91 Main Street, Bingley, West Yorkshire BD16 2JA
Telephone 01274 562402

Bingley Trail

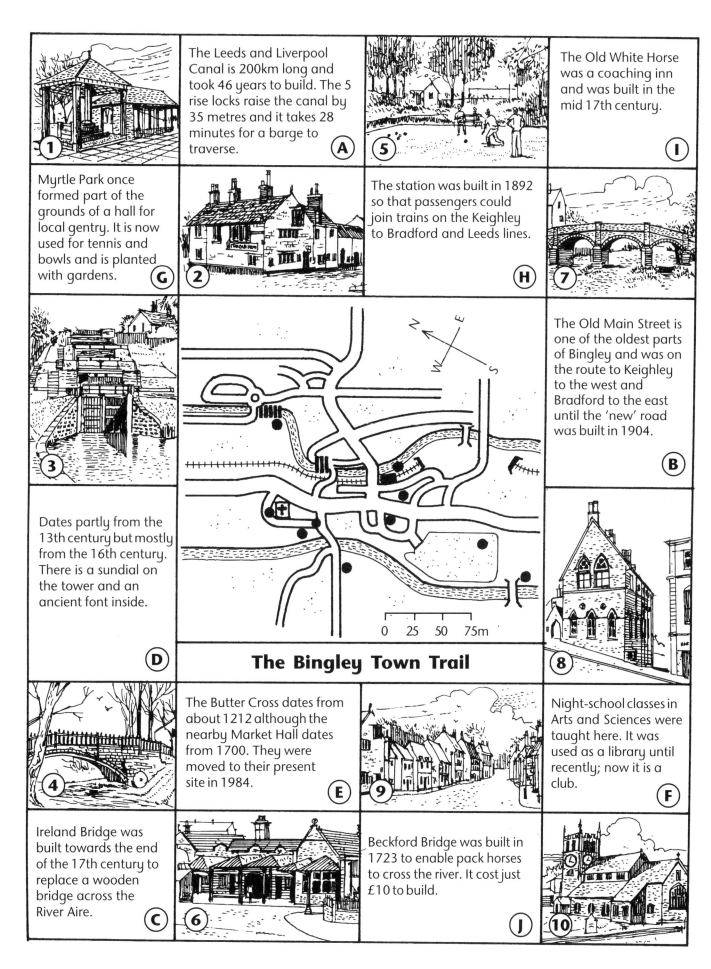

(1)

A The Leeds and Liverpool Canal is 200km long and took 46 years to build. The 5 rise locks raise the canal by 35 metres and it takes 28 minutes for a barge to traverse.

(5)

I The Old White Horse was a coaching inn and was built in the mid 17th century.

G Myrtle Park once formed part of the grounds of a hall for local gentry. It is now used for tennis and bowls and is planted with gardens.

(2)

H The station was built in 1892 so that passengers could join trains on the Keighley to Bradford and Leeds lines.

(7)

(3)

B The Old Main Street is one of the oldest parts of Bingley and was on the route to Keighley to the west and Bradford to the east until the 'new' road was built in 1904.

D Dates partly from the 13th century but mostly from the 16th century. There is a sundial on the tower and an ancient font inside.

0 25 50 75m

The Bingley Town Trail

(8)

(4)

E The Butter Cross dates from about 1212 although the nearby Market Hall dates from 1700. They were moved to their present site in 1984.

(9)

F Night-school classes in Arts and Sciences were taught here. It was used as a library until recently; now it is a club.

C Ireland Bridge was built towards the end of the 17th century to replace a wooden bridge across the River Aire.

(6)

J Beckford Bridge was built in 1723 to enable pack horses to cross the river. It cost just £10 to build.

(10)

Investigating Rivers

These activity sheets provide an introduction to aspects of the water cycle, local water dispersal and river study. Fieldwork is an important part of this unit and an organised river study is a useful way to help children understand the form and function of rivers. Choose a section of river or stream close to the school that has good access, is safe, and is surrounded by land used in a variety of ways. The best sections will have areas of erosion, deposition and undercutting.

Learning Objectives

- To understand the process of the water cycle.
- To become familiar with the vocabulary used to describe it.
- To consider the effects of the dispersal of rainfall.
- To understand how weather conditions affect evaporation.
- To use local maps of different scales, and atlases.
- To describe sequentially a journey along a river, citing the features seen.

Water Cycle

Introducing and using the sheet
- Talk about rainfall, where it comes from and where it goes. Consider each part of the water cycle and ask the children to think why western areas of the UK are wetter than eastern areas. (Prevailing winds come from the west and most of the rainfall lands on the areas of higher land, also in the west.)
- Introduce the activity sheet and ask the children to put the correct label in each box. Ensure that the water-cycle vocabulary is used and learned.

Follow-up/extension ideas
- Hand out atlases and look at the distribution of rainfall across the UK. Ask the children to draw graphs highlighting the differences between the wetter west and the drier east.
- Talk through the water cycle using a large annotated display.

Go with the Flow

Introducing and using the sheet
- On a map of the school, identify places where rainwater collects after heavy rain, such as roofs, playing fields and playgrounds, and ask the children what they think happens to that rainwater. Encourage them to describe how the majority returns to the sea.
- Look at an atlas map showing the distribution of rivers in the UK. Ask the children to find rivers close to your town.

Follow-up/extension ideas
- Measure rates of evaporation in the school playground. Small groups of children can use chalk to trace the changing outline of a puddle at 15-minute intervals until it disappears. (Rates of evaporation will vary according to the weather so adjust recording intervals accordingly.) Encourage the children to describe the weather conditions that promote maximum evaporation (warm, sunny, windy).
- Look in atlases at the river closest to your town and help the children locate the source, the towns it passes through, the sea it flows into and to work out its length.

Down by the Riverside

Introducing and using the sheet
- Choose a river on a local 1:50 000 or 1:25 000 scale map and ask the children to trace its course over 5 kilometres. They should identify river features, nearby physical features and human activity alongside the river.
- Look at the activity sheet and trace the course of the river, talking about the countryside it passes through and describing the river at various points. Explain to the children the process of erosion and deposition and tell them which parts of the river are fastest and which slowest (the inside bends, where deposition occurs, are slowest; the outside bends, where erosion occurs, are fastest).

Follow-up/extension ideas
- Ask the children to construct a land-use map, with a colour code and key, based on the land on the activity sheet.
- Repeat the activities on the sheet using a large-scale map (1:1 250) of a nearby river.

Water Cycle

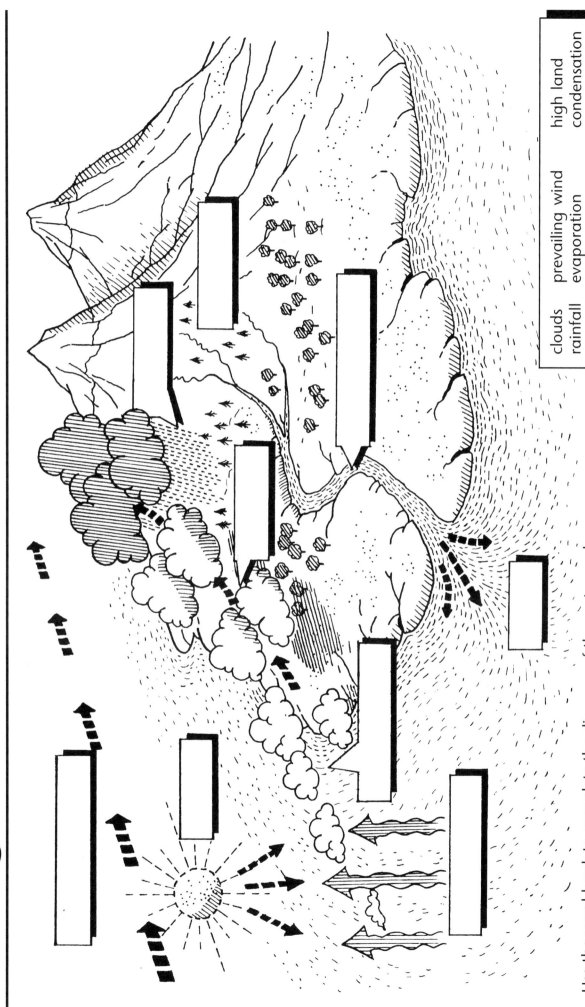

Word bank:

clouds prevailing wind high land
rainfall evaporation condensation
sea rivers and streams sun

- Use the word-bank to complete the diagram of the water cycle.
- Write a description of the water cycle using all of the words in the word-bank.

Go with the Flow

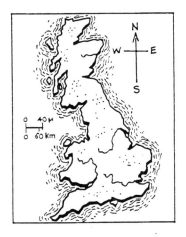

● Use an atlas to find out the names of the towns these rivers pass through. Mark them on the maps.

● Make a chart, like the one on the right, giving information about each of the four rivers. Add another four of your own.

River	Trent	Dee	Thames	Severn
Source				
Towns the river flows through/ near				
Length in km				
Sea it flows into				

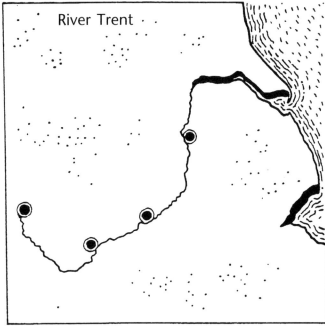

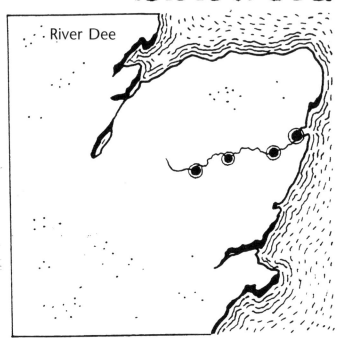

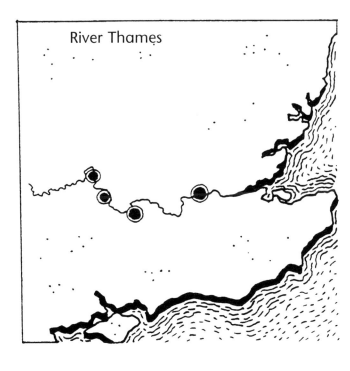

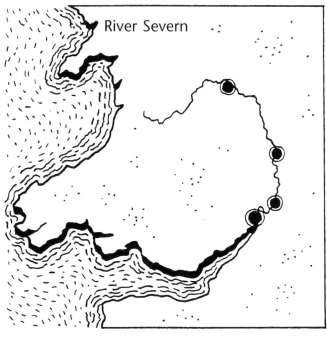

Down by the Riverside

- Describe a walk along the riverbank from left to right.
- Measure the width of the river at the start, middle and end of the walk.
- Mark where you think erosion is occurring and deposition is occurring.

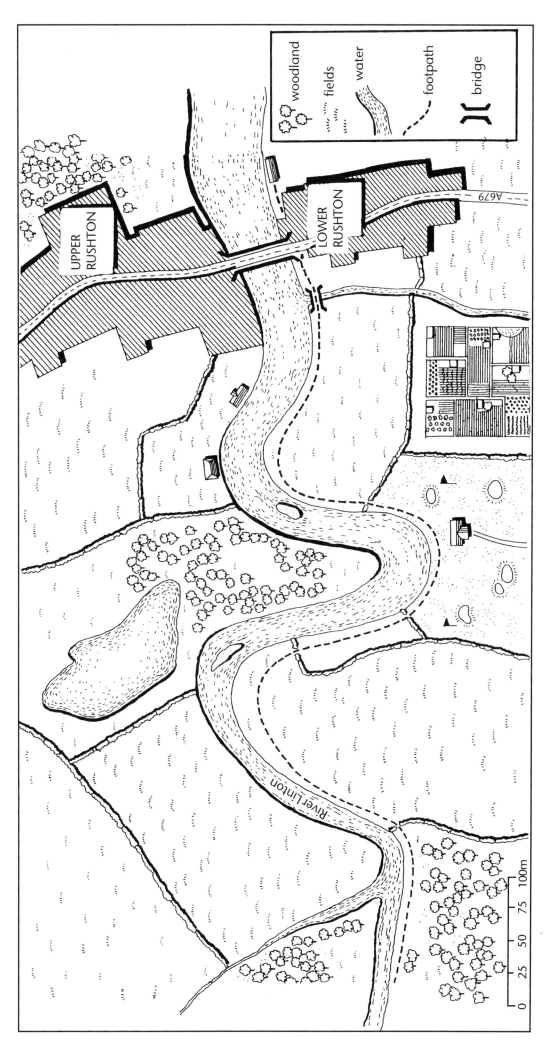

ideas page

The Mountain Environment

Background

This unit looks at the unique environment of mountains, which show similar features throughout the world. The activity sheets should be used to contrast the mountain environment with that of the children's locality, as well as with other environments on the planet such as deserts and rain forests. The sheets look at the general characteristics and climate of the mountain environment.

Learning Objectives

- To identify how features vary between different environments.
- To find out about the distribution of mountain environments.
- To compare mountain environments.
- To use secondary sources.

Where in the World?

Introducing and using the sheet
- Encourage the children to name different kinds of natural environments.
- Look at the activity sheet and talk about each of the environments shown in terms of landscape, climate and vegetation.
- Hand around atlases (make sure they contain both physical and political maps). Ask the children to locate an example of each of the environments shown on the activity sheet, looking first at the physical and then the political map, and to enter the name of the example environment in each box.

Follow-up/extension ideas
- Conduct research into each of the five environments shown. The children should use ICT (especially video, if possible) to find out more about each one.
- Ask the children to collect pictures and photographs showing views of each of the environments and make a display with captions.

Mountain File

Introducing and using the sheet
- On a local 1:50 000 scale map show the children areas of higher land (concentrations of contour lines) and ask them to make a relief map of your area.
- Look in greater detail at mountain environments using an atlas. Name the ranges that the children can find, the continents they are located in and the highest peaks.
- Talk about the activity sheet. Encourage the children to note the location of each mountain environment, its direction and distance from London or your town, its highest peak, its climate and any evidence of human activity.

Follow-up/extension ideas
- Ask small groups of children to produce a file or leaflet on a chosen mountain environment, including pictures, maps and other information. They should use atlases, books and CD-ROMs.
- Ask each group to give a short presentation on their mountain environment, perhaps using images and text produced in Powerpoint or similar.

Comparing Climates

Introducing and using the sheet
- Look at the activity sheet and talk about a typical summer and winter day in each place.
- Ask the children to draw, or use ICT to create, climate graphs for each location and to compare the climate of one location with that of the others and of your own town. [A = Innsbruck, Austria; B = In Salah, Libya; C = Belém, Brazil; D = Lusaka, Zambia; E = Verkhoyansk, Siberia]

Follow-up/extension ideas
- Using newspapers, teletext or the Internet, the children could find out what the weather was like for these cities on the previous day, and what the forecast is for the next. They could compare each with the mountain environment.
- Talk about the weather characteristics of each environment, for example extreme heat, humidity or blizzards, and how they might affect human activity. Talk about Mt Kilimanjaro, the highest peak in Africa (Tanzania), and how it has an ice-cap on its summit and a rain forest on its lower slopes. Consider the phenomenon of how air cools with altitude (the sun heats the land and the land heats the air, so the further away the air is from the land, the colder it is).

Where in the World?

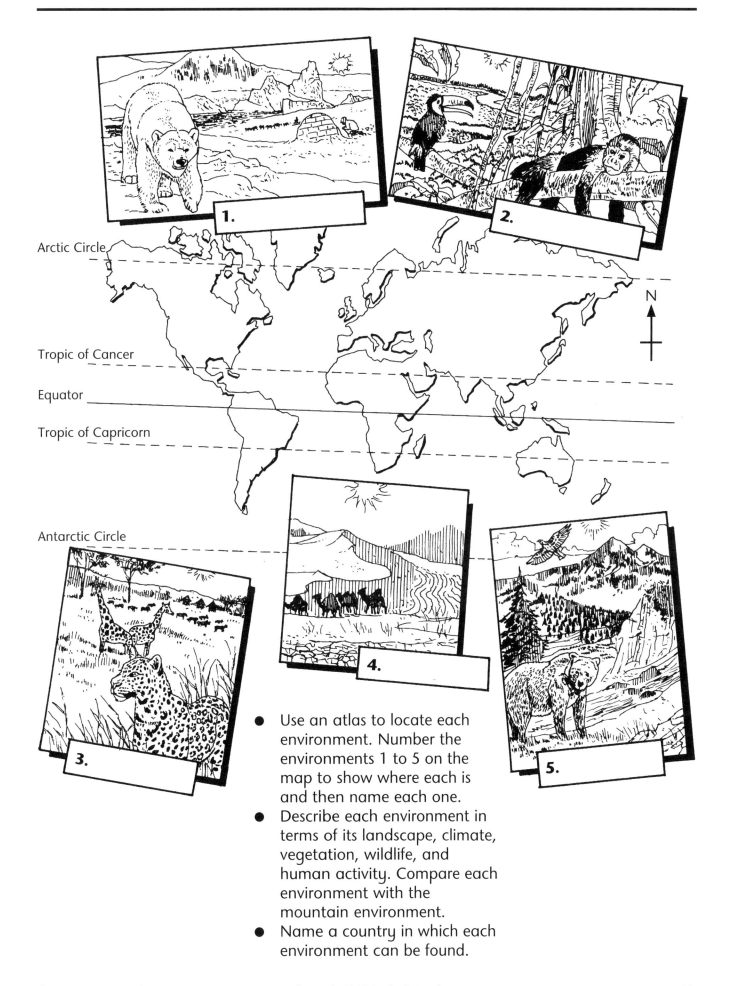

Arctic Circle

Tropic of Cancer

Equator

Tropic of Capricorn

Antarctic Circle

N

1.

2.

3.

4.

5.

- Use an atlas to locate each environment. Number the environments 1 to 5 on the map to show where each is and then name each one.
- Describe each environment in terms of its landscape, climate, vegetation, wildlife, and human activity. Compare each environment with the mountain environment.
- Name a country in which each environment can be found.

Mountain File

- Use an atlas to complete the chart.
- Draw lines from the chart to the map to show the location of each mountain range.
- Use books, atlases, CD-ROMs and the Internet to find out more about each mountain range.

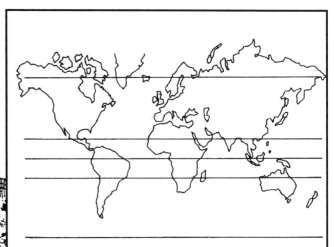

Mountain Range	Continent	Direction from London	Distance from London	Highest Peak	Height	Human Activity (towns/climate)
Lake District	Europe					
Grampians			550km			
Alps						Many towns – Innsbruck, Chamonix, Grenoble. Cold winter, mild summer.
Pyrenees		South				
Rockies	N. America					
Andes						Some villages and towns. La Paz. High lakes. Cold winter May–Sept.
Atlas				Mt Toubkal	4165m	
Urals			4500km			
Himalayas					8848m	
Great Divide						

Geography Highlights for Juniors 2

Comparing Climates

Innsbruck

A.

	J	F	M	A	M	J	Jy	A	S	O	N	D
Max°C	-3	0	5	10	14	17	19	18	15	9	4	-1
Rain mm	53	46	38	56	74	104	130	114	79	61	56	48

Cape Town

Sydney

B.

	J	F	M	A	M	J	Jy	A	S	O	N	D
Max°C	21	24	29	34	38	43	44	44	41	35	27	22
Rain mm	3	3	0	0	0	0	0	0	0	0	5	3

London

C.

	J	F	M	A	M	J	Jy	A	S	O	N	D
Max°C	26	26	27	27	27	27	26	26	27	27	27	27
Rain mm	318	359	359	320	260	170	150	111	89	84	66	155

Verkhoyansk

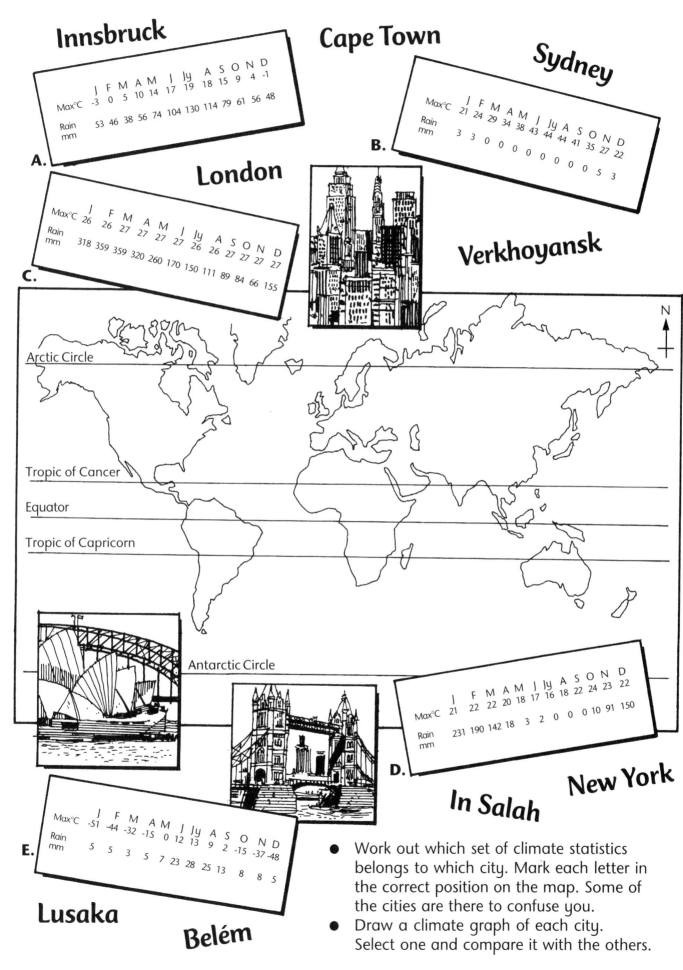

Arctic Circle

Tropic of Cancer

Equator

Tropic of Capricorn

Antarctic Circle

N

D.

	J	F	M	A	M	J	Jy	A	S	O	N	D
Max°C	21	22	22	20	18	17	16	18	22	24	23	22
Rain mm	231	190	142	18	3	2	0	0	0	10	91	150

In Salah

New York

E.

	J	F	M	A	M	J	Jy	A	S	O	N	D
Max°C	-51	-44	-32	-15	0	12	13	9	2	-15	-37	-48
Rain mm	5	5	3	5	7	23	28	25	13	8	8	5

Lusaka

Belém

- Work out which set of climate statistics belongs to which city. Mark each letter in the correct position on the map. Some of the cities are there to confuse you.
- Draw a climate graph of each city. Select one and compare it with the others.

Tourism

Mountain environments are important for tourism. In winter they provide ideal conditions for skiing and snowboarding and in summer for walking or horse-riding. **Chamonix** and **The Holiday Business** consider the seasonal aspects of tourism in Chamonix, in the French Alps. **Carry on Camping** looks at a contrasting environment – the desert – and the problems and issues facing people who explore it.

Learning Objectives

- To understand how weather conditions and environment affect human activity.
- To recognise the effects of tourism on an area.
- To use secondary sources.

Chamonix

Introducing and using the sheet

- Locate Chamonix on a map of Europe and ask the children to identify the type of countryside that it is in.
- Discuss what the weather is like in winter, spring, summer and autumn and which conditions might be the most popular with holiday-makers.
- Use the activity sheet to study Chamonix in the summer and the winter. Talk about the different kinds of holidays possible there and the different kinds of people they would appeal to.

Follow-up/extension ideas

- Hand around holiday brochures for the children to find destinations where different kinds of holidays can be had in different seasons. Ask them each to make a brochure page advertising the same resort, but at different times of year. Make a collage of their tourist brochures.
- Ask the children to write postcards home from the resort during either summer or winter. They should sketch the resort on the front and on the reverse describe the weather and what activities are offered at that time.

The Holiday Business

Introducing and using the sheet

- Talk about the 'business process' whereby raw materials come into a factory and finished products leave to be sold. For example, in a factory making potato crisps inputs will be potatoes, cooking oil, flavourings, packaging, labour and energy, and outputs will be crisps and waste products.
- Explain how the process of inputs and outputs operates in other types of business, including travel, and how this affects the lives of local people and the environment.
- Look at the activity sheet and talk about some of the likely costs and benefits of tourism to an area. Positive inputs may be money and facilities, including improved communications and medical care and more employment. Negative aspects may be higher living costs, increased traffic, litter, noise and pollution, forest clearance for ski runs and increased avalanche risks.

Follow-up/extension ideas

- Explain to the children how tourism has affected a different environment, perhaps somewhere close to the school or a new tourist amenity in a developing country.

Carry on Camping

Introducing and using the sheet

- Ask the children to think about travelling and camping in the UK, including what items they would take.
- Repeat the above but ask the children to think what additional items they would take to potentially dangerous environments such as polar areas.
- Introduce the activity sheet and talk about each of the items, but do not comment on their usefulness in an emergency. The children should work in pairs.
- Ask the pairs to circle their ten items and make a separate list saying why each would be useful. Repeat the exercise but this time for walking and camping in a mountain environment.

Follow-up/extension ideas

- Ask the children to plan a camping holiday to Chamonix using holiday brochures and the Internet. They should work out the shortest route when driving from their home, how far this journey is and how long it will take – remind them to add in the ferry crossing.
- Ask the children to make posters warning tourists of the hazards of mountain environments in summer and winter.

Chamonix

- Describe the different holidays a winter and a summer tourist would have in Chamonix.

Date 20 January   Time 1pm   Temperature -5°C
Chamonix is a fascinating town set amongst spectacular scenery at the foot of Mont Blanc, the highest peak of the Alps. It has a long-standing reputation amongst skiers who come to ski the famous Vallée Blanche. There is steep mountain skiing, deep powder chutes, 136km of prepared pistes – quite simply the most extreme skiing you will ever encounter.

Hotel Morgane – special attractions
Located close to the cable car; outdoor heated swimming pool; sauna; sleigh rides; ice hockey.

Date 20 July   Time 1pm   Temperature 25°C
This is ideal walking country with spectacular scenery, fresh mountain air and charming little hamlets. There are 310km of marked trails for keen walkers to explore. Along the flower-lined streets are numerous galleries and outdoor restaurants to enjoy, or simply sit outside and soak in the warm air and summer sunshine.

Hotel Morgane – special attractions
Breakfast terrace; outdoor pool and water slide; barbecue area; gardens and picnic

The Holiday Business

Tourism affects Chamonix and places like it in a variety of ways.

● Think of five ways in which tourism may be good for Chamonix and five ways in which it may be bad.

GOOD POINTS

1. _____
2. _____
3. _____
4. _____
5. _____

BAD POINTS

1. _____
2. _____
3. _____
4. _____
5. _____

Geography Highlights for Juniors 2

Carry on Camping

Help pack the four-wheeler for a desert expedition:

● Circle the ten items you think would be the most important to take with you.

Connecting Ourselves to the World

Background

These activity sheets can be used or modified for use in different year groups to help children study how we communicate or travel. They could be used to support work in other subjects and provide a geographical component to ongoing work.

Learning Objectives

- To understand why we use different modes of communication.
- To recognise weather patterns and weather symbols.
- To see how different places can be reached by air.
- To use and interpret weather reports and timetables.

You've Got Mail

Introducing and using the sheet
- Discuss how the school communicates with other people and organisations. Talk about how, when and where the school receives and sends its mail, telephone calls, faxes and emails.
- Look at the different places the school in the activity sheet communicated with and find them in an atlas. (The boxes could be blanked out or adapted for your school. They could be completed with the help of administrative staff over the course of one, two, three days or a week depending on the volume of communication your school has with other places.)

Follow-up/extension ideas
- Look at which forms of communication were used most often and discuss why the children think some forms of communication were used instead of others.
- Ask the children to make one map showing the outgoing communications your school makes and another showing the school's incoming communications (the data should be based on a completed school copy of the activity sheet). The maps could be A3 in size and entitled 'Places that we communicate with' and 'Places that communicate with us'.

MetFax

Introducing and using the sheet
- Talk about the patterns of the UK climate. The north is cooler than the south in summer, the west is wetter than the east, north-eastern and highland areas receive more snow.
- Explain what the weather symbols shown on the activity sheet represent and how they are used.

Follow-up/extension ideas
- Twin with a school elsewhere in the UK for a set period of time, perhaps over the Internet, and exchange local weather information. Ask the children to draw graphs, or produce them on a spreadsheet, showing the weather each school is experiencing and then to explain the differences. Alternatively, weather information can be collected from broadsheet newspapers or teletext pages.
- Obtain a MetFax issued by the Met Office. Look at the forecast for your region and for that of the twin school and ask the children to record how accurate each is over the course of the following week.

Come Fly With Me

Introducing and using the sheet
- Talk about travelling by air and explain the process of checking in to board an aeroplane. Ask if any of the children have flown and, if so, where they flew to. Ask them to map the results of the whole class.
- Locate places in the world that you have studied and look at the journeys to them by air. Describe one or two of the journeys to the children, who should follow on an atlas. Then ask them to get into pairs and each describe some of the other journeys to their partner.
- Look at the activity sheet. The children should use an atlas to locate Leeds and Bradford Airport and the places listed on the departures board on the sheet.

Follow-up/extension ideas
- Conduct a similar survey on departures from your local airport. The children could use timetables or teletext to get information. Complete the survey over one hour for a large airport such as Heathrow or one week for a small one.
- Make a wall display using a large map. Ask the children to map routes, add flight times and enhance the display with model aeroplanes and airline logos.

You've Got Mail

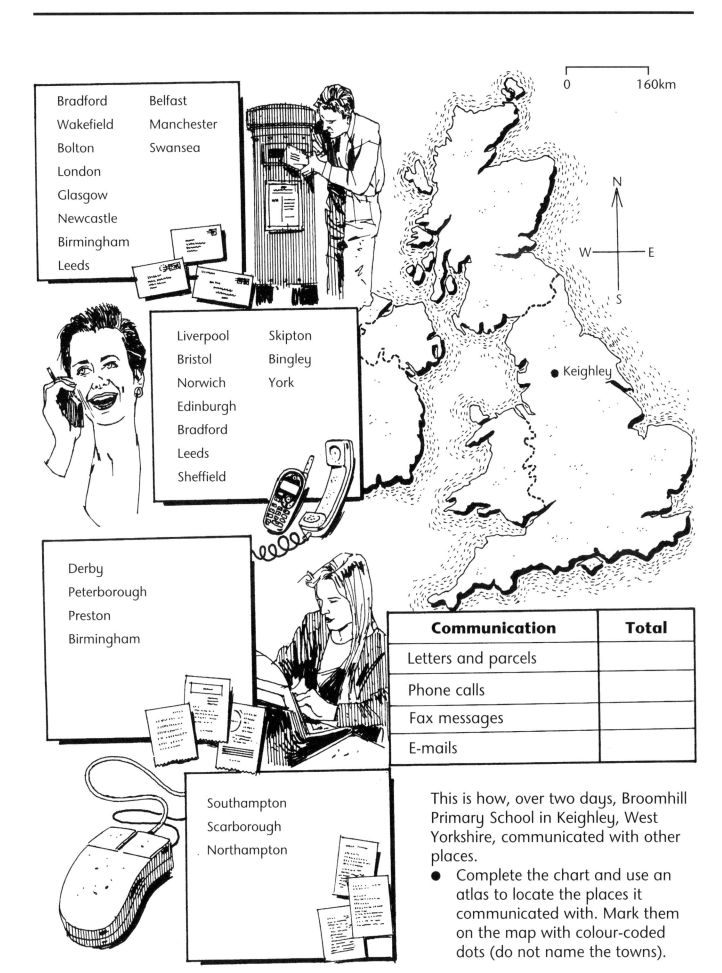

Bradford	Belfast
Wakefield	Manchester
Bolton	Swansea
London	
Glasgow	
Newcastle	
Birmingham	
Leeds	

Liverpool	Skipton
Bristol	Bingley
Norwich	York
Edinburgh	
Bradford	
Leeds	
Sheffield	

Derby
Peterborough
Preston
Birmingham

Southampton
Scarborough
Northampton

0 ——— 160km

• Keighley

N
W — E
S

Communication	Total
Letters and parcels	
Phone calls	
Fax messages	
E-mails	

This is how, over two days, Broomhill Primary School in Keighley, West Yorkshire, communicated with other places.

- Complete the chart and use an atlas to locate the places it communicated with. Mark them on the map with colour-coded dots (do not name the towns).

MetFax

- Use an atlas to mark the towns below on the weather forecaster's map.
- Using the weather-fax information for each place, construct a weather map for the UK showing the weather now and, on another copy of the map, the forecast for later. Use the appropriate weather symbols.

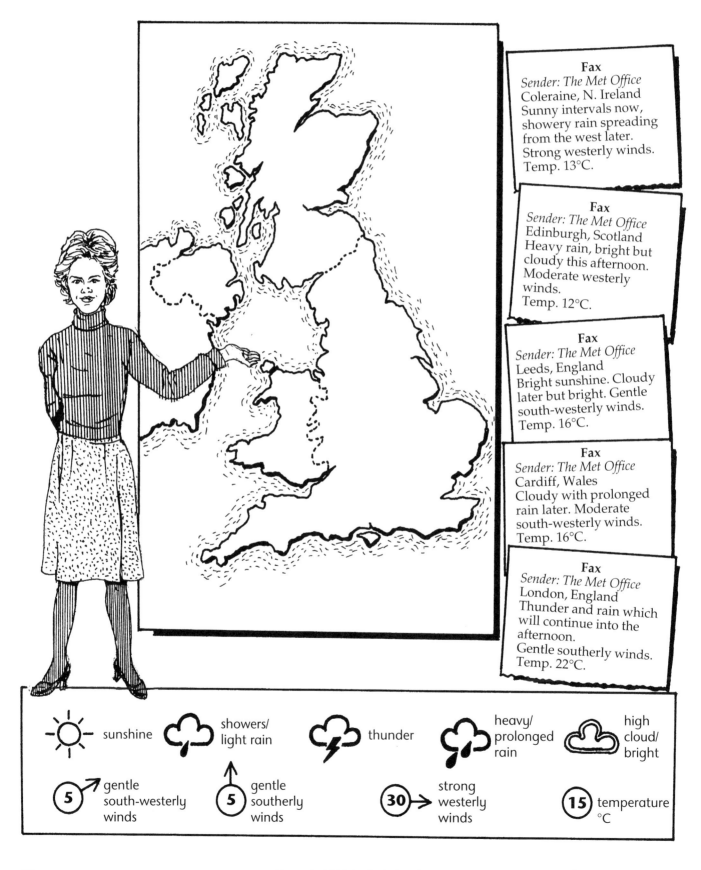

Fax
Sender: The Met Office
Coleraine, N. Ireland
Sunny intervals now,
showery rain spreading
from the west later.
Strong westerly winds.
Temp. 13°C.

Fax
Sender: The Met Office
Edinburgh, Scotland
Heavy rain, bright but
cloudy this afternoon.
Moderate westerly
winds.
Temp. 12°C.

Fax
Sender: The Met Office
Leeds, England
Bright sunshine. Cloudy
later but bright. Gentle
south-westerly winds.
Temp. 16°C.

Fax
Sender: The Met Office
Cardiff, Wales
Cloudy with prolonged
rain later. Moderate
south-westerly winds.
Temp. 16°C.

Fax
Sender: The Met Office
London, England
Thunder and rain which
will continue into the
afternoon.
Gentle southerly winds.
Temp. 22°C.

sunshine | showers/light rain | thunder | heavy/prolonged rain | high cloud/bright

5 gentle south-westerly winds | 5 gentle southerly winds | 30 strong westerly winds | 15 temperature °C

Geography Highlights for Juniors 2

Come Fly With Me

- For each flight, work out the direction and distance the aircraft will fly and the approximate time it will take to get there at 500km per hour.
- Complete the map showing the aircraft routes from Leeds Bradford Airport.

LEEDS BRADFORD AIRPORT
DEPARTURES SATURDAY 20 JUNE

Time	Destination
07:30	Heathrow – London
07:40	Amsterdam
08:15	Dublin
09:00	Brussels
09:30	Jersey
10:20	Belfast
11:45	Paris
13:30	Edinburgh
15:15	Oslo
16:10	Tenerife
17:30	Rome
18:10	Prague
20:20	Alicante

Direction	Distance km	Flight time

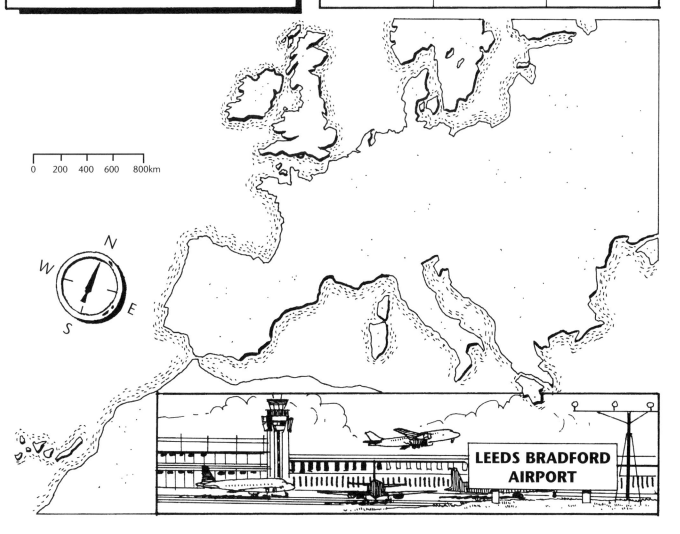

0 200 400 600 800km

Geography Highlights for Juniors 2

Local Traffic

Local traffic issues can take many forms, including bypass roads, traffic-calming measures and pedestrianisation of a shopping centre. These issues have considerable impact on a local community and on the environment in which they are situated.

It is important also to study other environmental issues such as the development of a quarry, reservoir or wind farm or the development of a retail park on the outskirts of a town or city. These activity sheets should be used to aid the study of local issues.

Learning Objectives

- To find out about the issues involved in a change in the use of the local environment.
- To make important planning decisions, explain them and consider the consequences.
- To consider other people's points of view.
- To use and interpret large-scale maps.

NIMBY

Introducing and using the sheet

- Talk about how and why the volume of traffic has increased (around 14m vehicle-users in 1980, 18m in 1990, 25m in 2001 – greater personal wealth and leisure time and a decline in public transport). Ask the children how this will affect our quality of life, and pressure on the land.
- Ask the children to consider the effects that building a new road will have on people's lives. Who do they think will 'win' and who 'lose'?
- Look at the activity sheet. Explain that the two roundabouts need to be connected by a new road. Look at the places that will be affected by the road or by the noise and pollution it creates. Ask the children to complete the sheet in pairs (tell them that new roads should avoid heavily built-up areas).

Follow-up/extension ideas

- Ask the pairs to list the kinds of people who may protest against each of their proposed routes and why. Tell the children that one kilometre of new road costs about £5 million to build. Ask them to calculate the cost of their new routes. Based on both the cost and the predicted views of local people, they should choose their preferred route.
- Talk about the 'NIMBY' (Not In My Back Yard) effect that occurs when large-scale building projects are planned. Ask each pair to choose someone who will be affected by their new road and to write, as this person, a letter of complaint to the local newspaper.

Headline News

Introducing and using the sheet

- This sheet should be used with the previous one, **NIMBY**. It relates to the children's preferred route between the two roundabouts.
- Talk about public inquiries and the people who protest against building schemes by climbing trees, digging tunnels or marching.
- Before asking the children to write the newspaper article on the activity sheet, talk about the layout of newspapers and impartiality of responsible journalists.

Follow-up/extension ideas

- Conduct a role-play of a public inquiry looking into one of the pairs' preferred route. Divide the class into interest groups. At the end, ask the children what they think should happen.

Close-up

Introducing and using the sheet

- Ask the children why a new road might need to be built in a town.
- Talk about the effects of new roads in urban areas; encourage the children to consider the effects on the environment and on property prices.
- Following the course of the new road on the activity sheet, talk about the road and the kinds of people that will be directly affected by it.

Follow-up/extension ideas

- Ask the children to write a paragraph about the effects of the new road on the community.
- Repeat the exercise using an extract of a local 1:1250 Ordnance Survey map that shows the school and some of the children's streets and houses. Add a new road cutting through the area similar to that shown on the activity sheet. Ask the children how they would feel about the new road being built so close to them. Ask them to consider how it would affect their lives and the lives of some local people and businesses.

NIMBY

- Work out two possible routes that a new road from Kirby to Crossflatts might take.
- List the places or areas that each proposed route would pass through or very close to.

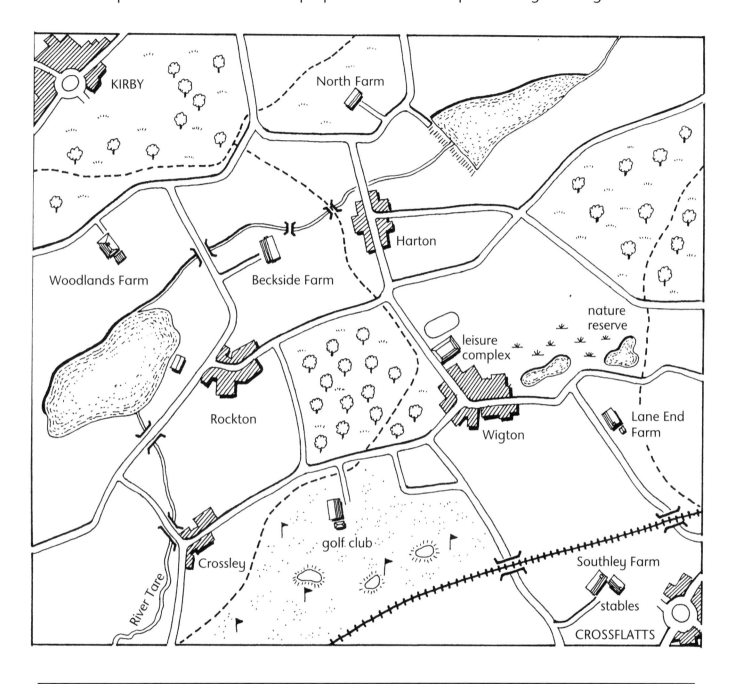

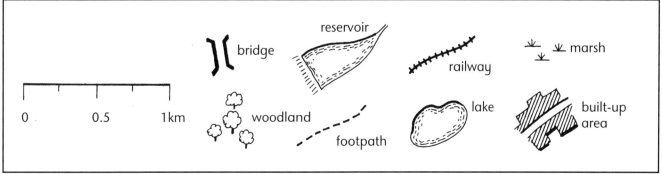

KIRBY

North Farm

Harton

Woodlands Farm

Beckside Farm

nature reserve

leisure complex

Rockton

Wigton

Lane End Farm

Crossley

golf club

River Tare

Southley Farm

stables

CROSSFLATTS

bridge	
reservoir	
railway	marsh
woodland	lake
footpath	built-up area

0   0.5   1km

Headline News

- Fill in the names of four people who will be affected by your road. Add the views of each.
- Imagine that you are a local journalist. Write about the proposed new road. Add three photographs (draw these) and a headline.

Geography Highlights for Juniors 2 © Folens (copiable page)

Close-up

● Fill in the speech balloons to say how the life of each of these people will change when the new road is built.

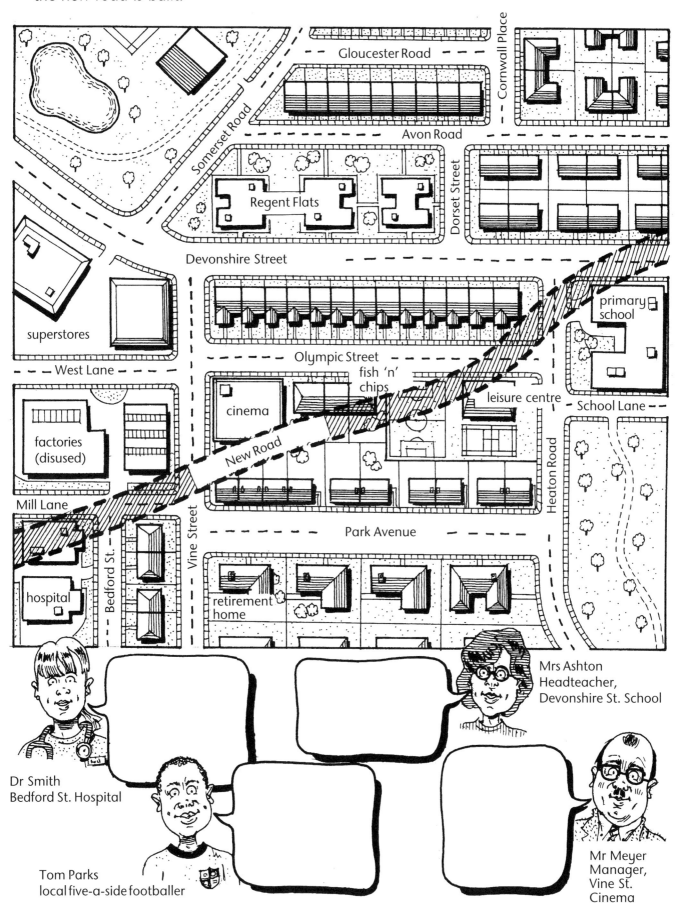

Investigating Coasts

Background

The coast is a unique environment as it is the meeting place of the land and the sea. Here the sea, with its enormous power and ability to transport huge amounts of material, sculpts the hard and soft rock that makes up the land. This results in the creation of a wide range of landforms. The activity sheets look at the form and range of features caused by erosion and deposition and consider the problems of protecting the coastal areas that are important to us.

Learning Objectives

- To use appropriate geographical vocabulary.
- To know about the physical features of coasts.
- To recognise the processes of erosion and deposition.
- To understand the nature of coastal protection.
- To use and interpret maps.

Carving the Coast

Introducing and using the sheet

- Ask the children to relate their experiences of the coast and seaside holidays.
- Talk about the power of the sea and how it shapes the coast.
- Consider the differences between shingle and sand on beaches and how they affect the way that the beach is used.
- Explain how landforms are produced by the waves eroding the rocks and how hard rock erodes slowly, producing headlands, while soft rock erodes more quickly, producing bays.
- Talk through how the coastal landforms shown on the activity sheet were formed.

Follow-up/extension ideas

- Ask the children to draw a map from the sketch on the activity sheet. On it they should label the coastal landforms, signs of human activity and names of villages. They should also mark on areas of erosion and deposition.

Gulf Coast

Introducing and using the sheet

- Talk about the different activities that people enjoy at the coast and the kinds of landscape best suited to each activity – for example, sunbathing on a sandy beach. Ask the children what activities they have done on visits to the coast.
- Look at the coastline map on the activity sheet. Ask the children to talk about the landforms they can see.

Follow-up/extension ideas

- Ask the children to describe a walk along the coast following the footpath.
- Ask them to draw and label sketches from their viewpoint of what they can see as they walk.
- Using the map on the activity sheet and the information about the landscape and amenities, the children could each make a tourist leaflet, from an A4 sheet folded into three, advertising the Gulf Coast. Make a display of their leaflets.

Fighting the Sea

Introducing and using the sheet

- Talk about the destructive effect of waves and how they erode, transport and deposit material to create new landforms.
- Encourage the children to think about how the power of the sea can affect the lives of people who live and work at the coast.
- Talk through each type of storm damage on the activity sheet. Ask the children to suggest ways of reducing similar damage in the future.

Follow-up/extension ideas

- The children could write up the information on the activity sheet into a television news feature. They should say where the coast is (east Yorkshire), what has happened, how it has affected the lives of local people and what might be done to prevent it happening again in the future.
- Describe in more detail the effects of longshore drift (the removal of material from the east Yorkshire and Lincolnshire coast by strong sea currents) along this part of the coast, including on coastal inhabitants and housing. Use material to illustrate the damage caused to property, how villages along the coast have been lost to the sea and the formation of Spurn Head.

Carving the Coast

● Name the coastal features that you can see.

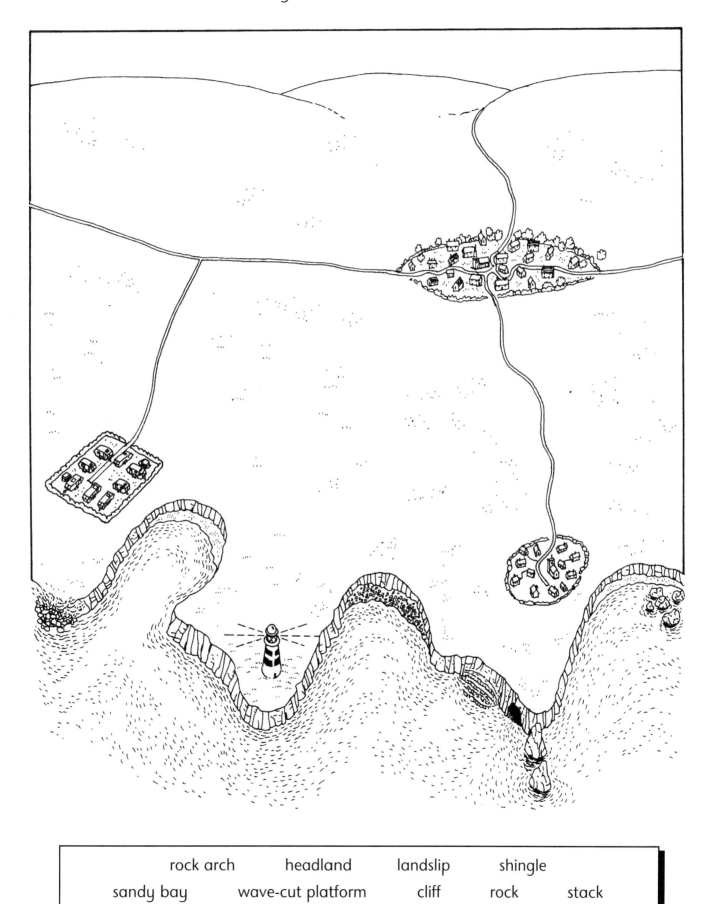

rock arch	headland	landslip	shingle
sandy bay	wave-cut platform	cliff	rock	stack

Gulf Coast

- Make up a symbol for each of these activities and locate it on the map in the most appropriate place.
- On the map put a viewpoint marker at a place where you would expect to get good views.

Activity	Symbol
Sunbathing	
Safe swimming	
Snorkelling	
Pedalos	
Rock climbing	
Horse-riding	
Paragliding	

- On the map put a 'P' where you think this photograph was taken from.

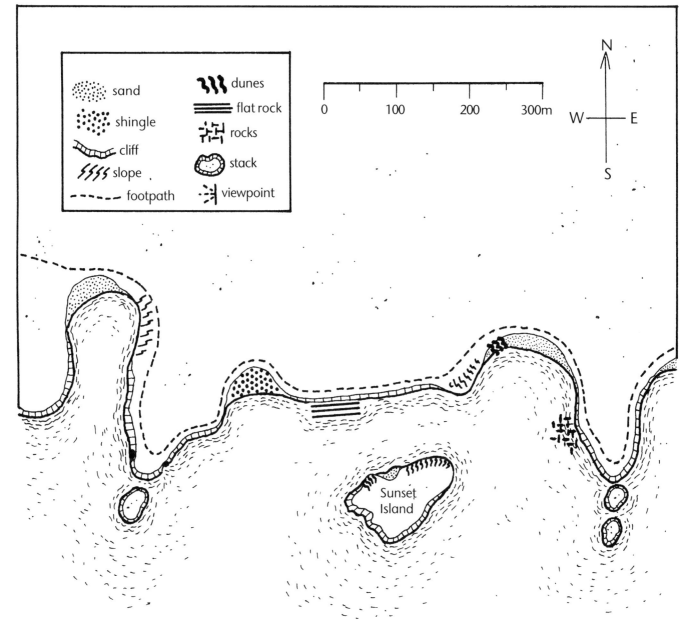

Fighting the Sea

The coast is an important place both for people who live and work there and people who visit.

- Look at the damages caused by a recent storm.
- Complete the sea defence reports and suggest a solution for each (either your own or one of those shown).

EAST YORKSHIRE SEA DEFENCE REPORT

by _____ (Council Officer)

Nature of problem/damage

Action needed

EAST YORKSHIRE SEA DEFENCE REPORT

by _____ (Council Officer)

Nature of problem/damage

Action needed

EAST YORKSHIRE SEA DEFENCE REPORT

by _____ (Council Officer)

Nature of problem/damage

Action needed

sea walls

groynes

blocks and boulders

Additional Information

Important mountain peaks

Mt Everest	Nepal/China	8 848m	29 028ft
K2 (Mt Godwin-Austen)	Pakistan/China	8 611m	28 250ft
Aconcagua	Argentina	6 960m	22 834ft
Mt McKinley	USA	6 194m	20 320ft
Kilimanjaro	Tanzania	5 896m	19 344ft
Mt Elbrus	Russia	5 642m	18 510ft
Mont Blanc	France/Italy	4 807m	15 770ft
Matterhorn	Switzerland	4 478m	14 691ft
Mt Fuji	Japan	3 776m	12 388ft
Mt Cook	New Zealand	3 764m	12 349ft
Ben Nevis	Scotland	1 343m	4 406ft
Vesuvius	Italy	1 277m	4 190ft
Snowdon	Wales	1 085m	3 560ft
Carrauntoohil	Ireland	1 041m	3 414ft
Scafell Pike	England	978m	3 206ft

Natural environments – river features

Source	The point on high land where a river begins.
Rapids	Fast-flowing water over and around rocks.
Waterfall	A cascade of water caused by a vertical change in the direction of the land.
Tributary	A stream or river that joins the main river.
Confluence	The point at which a tributary joins a river.
Drainage basin	An area of high land drained by a river.
Meander	The lower section of a river that continuously changes direction because of the hardness of the land it passes through.
Floodplain	A shallow river valley that floods during periods of prolonged rain.
Estuary	The part of a river close to the sea that floods twice a day at high tide.
Mouth	The point at which the river joins the sea.

Road distances from Bingley in kilometres

Aberdeen	540	Lincoln	140
Aberystwyth	240	Liverpool	110
Birmingham	180	London	330
Brighton	420	Manchester	65
Cambridge	235	Newcastle	170
Carlisle	290	Northampton	225
Edinburgh	320	Norwich	290
Exeter	460	Oxford	290
Glasgow	310	Penzance	620
Hull	110	Sheffield	75
Inverness	620	Southampton	370
Leeds	15	York	50

Wettest and driest

	J	F	M	A	M	J	J	A	S	O	N	D	TOTAL
Ambleside	214	146	112	101	90	111	134	139	184	196	209	215	1851
Cambridge	49	35	36	37	45	45	58	55	51	51	54	41	557

MetFax statistics		J	F	M	A	M	J	J	A	S	O	N	D	TOTAL
Coleraine	Temp°C	6	7	9	12	15	18	18	18	16	13	9	7	
	Rain mm	80	52	50	48	62	68	94	77	80	83	72	90	845
Edinburgh	Temp°C	5	6	8	11	14	17	19	18	16	12	8	6	
	Rain mm	59	51	38	38	51	49	61	67	60	63	66	55	658
Leeds	Temp°C	6	7	10	13	16	19	20	20	18	14	10	7	
	Rain mm	59	46	37	41	50	50	62	68	55	56	65	50	639
Cardiff	Temp°C	7	7	10	13	16	19	20	21	18	14	10	8	
	Rain mm	108	72	63	65	76	63	89	97	99	109	116	108	1065
London	Temp°C	6	7	10	13	17	20	22	21	19	14	10	7	
	Rain mm	54	40	37	37	46	45	57	59	49	57	64	48	593